ESSENTIAL SKILLS

Ancient Egypt's great pyramids are built 4,500 years ago.

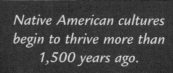

Ancient China rises to power more than 2,000 years ago.

Native American cultures begin to thrive more than 1,500 years ago.

OUR WORLD

NEAR & FAR

by Nancy Daniel Vest and Lisa Arnold

Columbus sails to the Americas. 1492

Powhatan leads over 30 Virginia Indian Tribes. 1600

George Washington leads the Revolutionary War. 1776

Abraham Lincoln writes Emancipation Proclamation. 1863

Susan B Anthony begins fight for women's rights. 1869

Helen Keller learns her first words. 1886

Jackie Robinson joins Major League Baseball. 1947

Martin Luther King leads March on Washington. 1963

FIVE PONDS PRESS

SOL NEWS

SOCIAL STUDIES IN SECOND GRADE

Social Studies Standards of Learning

Your child's Social Studies curriculum is determined by the Virginia State Department of Education. Students in Kindergarten through Third Grade work on preparing for the Social Studies Standards of Learning Test. This test is given at the end of Third Grade and covers all the material learned in Grades K-3.

Students in Second Grade will be taking tests throughout the year to determine their understanding of the material and to help them become familiar with test taking skills.

SOL Newsletters

As each new topic is introduced, you will receive an SOL Newsletter. In the newsletter, you will see the Standard of Learning being covered in class along with the Essential Questions and Essential Knowledge. These come directly from the State Department of Education.

The Essential Knowledge is the information which the State of Virginia expects your child to know to be successful on the Third Grade Standards of Learning Test.

The Essential Questions are also a reflection of what the State expects your child to know. Repeated review of these questions will help your child master the information.

The newsletter also contains a section called Learning at Home. Here you will find explanations of key points of the essential knowledge and activities to do at home.

These are just a few things which your child will study in Second Grade:

• The responsibilities of a good citizen;
• The way our community has changed over time in terms of buildings, jobs, transportation, and population;
• The contributions of ancient Egypt and China;
• The lives and contributions of American Indian cultures including the Powhatan, the Lakota, and the Pueblo peoples;
• How George Washington, Abraham Lincoln, Susan B. Anthony, Helen Keller, Jackie Robinson, and Martin Luther King, Jr. worked to improve the lives of all Americans;
• The construction of simple maps;
• Naming and locating the continents and oceans;
• Locating selected countries, rivers, mountain ranges, and lakes on maps and globes;
• The relationship between environment and culture;
• Differences between human, natural, and capital resources;
• State and local governments are run by elected officials;
• People in Virginia have diverse ethnic origins and traditions but are united by the sharing of common American principles.

Learning at Home

Help build your child's background knowledge as you talk with them every day.

• Get a library card. Check out books to read together.
• Be on the lookout for a globe, a world map, and a U.S. map for your home. Hang a world map in your child's room. Use small post-it notes or stickers to mark the places studied.
• As you travel, show your child maps of the route. Free maps of Virginia are available at the Virginia Department of Transportation.
• Work together with your child to draw maps of your home, your neighborhood, or even imaginary places.
• Trips to museums and historical sites help children develop understanding of social studies topics. Even a trip to the grocery store can lead to discussions of various countries and cultures around the world.
• Look for opportunities to enrich your child's experiences but more importantly, enjoy every moment of this special year together.

SECOND GRADE

S O L NEWS

CITIZENSHIP

Social Studies Standards of Learning
STANDARD 2.10

The student will explain the responsibilities of a good citizen, with emphasis on
a) Respecting and protecting the rights and property of others;
b) Taking part in the voting process when making classroom decisions;
c) Describing actions that can improve the school and community;
d) Demonstrating self-discipline and self-reliance;
e) Practicing honesty and trustworthiness.

Essential Question

What are some responsibilities of a good citizen?

Essential Knowledge

Responsibilities of a good citizen:
• Respecting and protecting the rights and property of others
• Taking part in the voting process when making classroom decisions
• Describing actions that can improve the school and community
• Demonstrating self-discipline and self-reliance
• Practicing honesty and trustworthiness

Learning At Home

All learning truly begins at home. You are your child's hero. Your son or daughter looks up to you as the example of the person he or she wants to be. It is a huge responsibility. You teach your child to be a good citizen every day with your actions, your response to difficulties, and the way you treat others.

• Talk with your child about the things you do to show good citizenship. Each day you show self-discipline and responsibility by honoring your commitments. You keep your word and strive to arrive at work and appointments on time. You do your chores without being reminded, take care of family members, attend school meetings, volunteer for various organizations, and vote in elections. You show respect for the property of others by not littering, cleaning up after your pets, and obeying the rules and laws. You may give up your seat for an older person, open the door for a stranger, fix a meal for a sick friend, or send a card of thanks to someone who shows you a kindness. All of these actions show your respect for others. Take the time to discuss the importance of these small acts of kindness with your child.

• When election time comes to your community, remember to vote. Talk to your child about the importance of having a voice in the leadership of your country. If possible, take your son or daughter with you on Election Day to see the procedures and processes involved.

• Think about ways you can work together as a family to improve your school or community. Perhaps you can volunteer for a local organization, sell lemonade for a good cause, donate used books to the library, collect toys for needy families, take food to a local food bank, or check on an elderly neighbor. There are hundreds of ways you can show your child how to become a caring and compassionate person. This is the essence of good citizenship.

BEING A GOOD CITIZEN

Name _____

Are these community helpers good citizens? Place a check mark next to each responsibility of a good citizen they show.

	DOCTOR	BUILDER	CHEF	SCIENTIST	TEACHER	POLICE
Respecting and protecting the property and rights of others						
Taking part in the voting process						
Striving to improve your school and community						
Having self-discipline						
Demonstrating self-reliance						
Being honest and trustworthy						

CLASSROOM COMMANDMENTS

Use this word bank to find out what makes you a super-cool student *and* a fantastic friend. Write the correct word in the blank. You will not use all the words.

TANTRUM	SELF-RELIANT	TRUTH
CHEAT	DISCIPLINE	SHARE
HELPER	RESPECT	COMMUNITY
FRIEND	PROPERTY	TRUSTWORTHY

1. It is never a good idea to __ __ __ __ __ on a test.

2. Showing __ __ __ __ __ __ __ means treating a person the way you would like to be treated.

3. A __ __ __ __ __ __ __ __ __ is a group of people living or working together.

4. Telling a lie is bad. You should always tell the __ __ __ __ __.

5. When you do all your chores without being told to, you are being __ __ __ __ - __ __ __ __ __ __ __ .

6. A good citizen respects the rights and __ __ __ __ __ __ __ __ of others.

7. When there are six cookies and twelve kids, one way everyone can have some is if they __ __ __ __ __.

8. A person who always does his or her best is __ __ __ __ __ __ __ __ __ __ __ __.

9. When people yell and stomp around, they are having a __ __ __ __ __ __ __.

10. A super student is a __ __ __ __ __ __ and a good __ __ __ __ __ __.

Use you social studies journal to write about the qualities of a good friend.

GOOD CITIZEN BALLOT

I vote for

_____

as our good citizen.

Here are some examples of good citizenship that I have seen:

Respecting and protecting the rights and property of others

_____

Helping to improve the school and community:

_____

Self-discipline:

_____

Self-reliance:

_____

Honesty:

_____

Trustworthiness:

_____

WHO'S IN CHARGE?

Name _____

Use your textbook or highlighted notes to fill in the chart below.

What is the name of our...	COUNTRY	STATE	CITY, COUNTY OR TOWN
	_____ _____	_____	_____ _____
Who is the highest elected official?			
What kinds of decisions do the elected officials make for the citizens?	Building the army and navy to keep our country safe.		

CHALLENGE: Explain how government officials are elected.

_____

_____

What happens if an elected official does not do a good job?

_____

_____

TEST TAKING PRACTICE 1

Name _____

Read It Once, Read It Twice

1   State and local government officials are —
- **A**   interviewed and then given a job
- **B**   elected by voters
- **C**   given the job by the President
- **D**   hired by the schools

Use the pictures to answer question 2.

2   Which action can improve your school or community?
- **F**   1
- **G**   2
- **H**   3
- **J**   4

3   Returning something that does not belong to you makes you —
- **A**   honest and trustworthy
- **B**   elected
- **C**   part of the voting process
- **D**   dishonest

VOCABULARY DEFINITIONS

Name _____

Key Word	Definition	Picture Clue
	Someone who by birth or choice is a member of a nation	
	Being able to control your impulses and urges	
	Being able to do things by yourself	
	Making people feel that they can depend on you to do a good job	

SOL NEWS

CIVICS

Social Studies Standards of Learning
STANDARD 2.12

The student will understand that the people of Virginia
a) Have state and local government officials who are elected by voters;
b) Have diverse ethnic origins, customs, and traditions, who make contributions to their communities, and who are united as Americans by common principles.

Essential Questions

• How are state and local government officials elected?
• How do people of diverse ethnic origins, customs, and traditions participate and contribute to their communities in the United States?
• How are people of different ethnic origins and customs united as Americans?

Essential Knowledge

• Voters in Virginia elect officials to make decisions for them in the state and local governments.
• People living in Virginia have diverse ethnic origins, customs, and traditions and participate in and contribute to their communities.
• People contribute to their community by practicing the responsibilities of good citizens.
• While people in our communities have different ethnic and cultural origins, they are united as Americans by common principles and traditions.
• People share the principles of respecting and protecting the rights and property of others, participating in school and community activities, demonstrating self-discipline and self-reliance, and practicing honesty and trustworthiness.

Learning At Home

• What are your family's customs and traditions? Do you spend Thanksgiving in a special place? Do you honor grandparents in special ways? How do you celebrate holidays? What types of foods do you eat? Remind your child of your family traditions and explain that every family is different. Each has its own special traditions and customs. The diversity of our people is what makes Virginia a great place to live.

• Appreciating the differences in others is one way to show respect. Remind kids that showing respect, being honest, and being trustworthy are qualities of good citizens. Encourage your child to recognize these qualities in themselves and others.

• Our country has a tradition of electing officials to try to solve problems and make our community better. When elections occur in your community, point out the campaign signs and discuss the various positions that will be decided. How are the winners chosen? What decisions will the officials have to make? Take your child to visit your town hall or county government offices.

• If possible plan a visit to the State Capitol in Richmond. Look in newspapers and magazines for pictures of our governor or other elected officials. Have your child write a letter to a local official offering a suggestion or thanking him or her for a school, a library, or a local park. Become involved in your community. Your involvement will serve as a model for your child.

OUR DIVERSE TRADITIONS

Name_____

Tradition	Country of origin	Draw it!	Does this make our country better?
Christmas Tree			
Halloween			
Karate			
Soccer			
Baseball			
Football			
Hip-hop and Jazz			

PROUD TO BE AN AMERICAN

Name _____

Americans are united by common principles and traditions.
Use your highlighted notes to fill in the blanks.

1. We believe in the right to life, _____,
and the pursuit of happiness.

2. When new people move to America, they learn to
speak _____.

3. Many will grow up to become citizens and
_____ in our elections.

4. On July 4th we celebrate _____.

5. On _____
we remember fallen soldiers.

6. On _____we honor people who
fought in our nation's wars.

7. We pledge _____
to our flag everyday in school.

8. We sing our _____
 at ball games.

TEST TAKING PRACTICE 2

Name _____

Dump the Junk

1 **The people of Virginia come from many different backgrounds, which means there is a lot of —**

A diversity

B sports parks

C government offices

D sameness

2 **How are all the different people in the United States united as Americans?**

F Everyone celebrates Valentine's Day.

G Each person owns an American flag.

H Americans share common principles and traditions.

J No one calls themselves an American.

3 **Americans share the common principles of self-discipline, self-reliance, and —**

A selfishness and bullying

B cheating

C playing basketball

D honesty and trustworthiness

PASSPORT PLEASE

PASSPORT/PASSEPORT
PASAPORTE

NATIONALITY / Nationalite´ / Nacionalidad

LAST NAME / Nom / Apellidos

GIVEN NAMES / Prenomes / Nombres

DATE OF BIRTH / Date de naissance / Fecha de nacimiento

PLACE OF BIRTH / Lieu de naissance / Lugar de nacimiento

SIGNATURE

DATE OF ISSUE / Date de de´liverance / Fecha de expedicion

VISA

Entries
Entrees / Entradas

Departures
Sorties / Salidas

VISAS

Entries
Entrees / Entradas

Departures
Sorties / Salidas

VOCABULARY DEFINITIONS

Name _____

Key Word	Definition	Picture Clue
	Differences between people such as religion or language	
	Ways of doing things that are passed from one generation to the next	
	The background of a person's family, including customs, language, and religion	
	Basic values or beliefs that shape behavior and help us make good choices	

SOL NEWS

The Powhatan of the Eastern Woodlands

Social Studies Standards of Learning
STANDARD 2.2, 2.4

The student will compare the lives and contributions of three American Indian cultures of the past and present with emphasis on the Powhatan of the Eastern Woodlands, the Lakota of the Plains, and the Pueblo peoples of the Southwest. The student will develop map skills by:
a) Locating the United States, China, and Egypt on world maps;
c) Locating the regions of the Powhatan, Lakota, and Pueblo Indians on United States maps;
d) Understanding the relationship between the environment and the culture of the Powhatan, Lakota, and Pueblo Indians.

Essential Questions

• In what ways were past American Indian lifestyles in Virginia similar to and different from those of the Lakota and Pueblo Indians?
• What are some contributions of American Indian culture to present-day life?
• How are American Indians of the past different from those of today?
Where are the regions of the Powhatan, Lakota, and Pueblo people located on a United States map?
• How did the environment affect the Powhatan, Lakota, and Pueblo Indians?
• How did the ancient Chinese, Egyptians, Powhatan, Lakota, and Pueblo people relate to their environment?

Essential Knowledge

TERMS TO KNOW
• **Culture:** The beliefs, customs, and way of life of a group of people
• **Regions:** Places that have common (the same) characteristics
• **Environment:** Surroundings
The Powhatan Indians lived in the Eastern Woodlands Region. They lived in wood frame houses with bark/reed covering. They were fishermen, hunters, and farmers. Walking and paddling canoes were their main forms of transportation. The land in the Eastern Woodland Region is made up of rivers, hills, mountains, and coastline. The Eastern Woodland Region has mild winters and hot, humid summers. The Powhatan farmed, fished, hunted, used trees for homes and canoes, and gathered plants for food.

Contributions of American Indians
• Arts (pottery, weaving, carving) • Knowledge of the environment
• Respect for nature • Farming of corn and tobacco

Changes in American Indian culture
• American Indian cultures have changed over time.
• Today American Indians live and work in Virginia and the United States.

Learning At Home

• We live in the Eastern Woodlands Region. Before the arrival of the English settlers, this land was home to the Powhatan people. They understood the environment and respected nature. The Powhatan prospered using the lands and waters around them. Thick woodlands gave them wood and bark for building homes, as well as for making bows, arrows, and spears for hunting and fishing. They made canoes by hollowing out the trunks of trees, then traveled on the rivers. The mild winters and hot, humid summers of our region were good for farming corn and tobacco. If corn or tobacco grows in your area, point out the fields to your child. Discuss other crops that grow in our climate.

• The lives of the Powhatan people were drastically changed by the arrival of the English settlers. A family visit to Jamestown would be a great way to build background knowledge about this time in history.

• The Chickahominy, Mattaponi, Nansemond, Pamunkey, Rappahannock, and Monacan Indians are some of the tribes in Virginia today. Look at a map of the state with your child. Try to locate the homes of these tribes. Some of them have museums or special events that are open to the public during the year. Be on the lookout for opportunities to learn more about their history and their plans for the future.

SECOND GRADE

S L NEWS

BULLETIN SIX

The Lakota of the Plains

Social Studies Standards of Learning
STANDARD 2.2, 2.4

The student will compare the lives and contributions of three American Indian cultures of the past and present with emphasis on the Powhatan of the Eastern Woodlands, the Lakota of the Plains, and the Pueblo peoples of the Southwest. The student will develop map skills by:

a) Locating the United States, China, and Egypt on world maps;

c) Locating the regions of the Powhatan, Lakota, and Pueblo Indians on United States maps;

d) Understanding the relationship between the environment and the culture of the Powhatan, Lakota, and Pueblo Indians.

Essential Questions

• In what ways were past American Indian lifestyles in Virginia similar to and different from those of the Lakota and Pueblo Indians?

• What are some contributions of American Indian culture to present-day life?

• How are American Indians of the past different from those of today?

• Where are the regions of the Powhatan, Lakota, and Pueblo people located on a United States map?

• How did the environment affect the Powhatan, Lakota, and Pueblo Indians?

• How did the ancient Chinese, Egyptians, Powhatan, Lakota, and Pueblo people relate to their environment?

Essential Knowledge

TERMS TO KNOW

• **Culture:** The beliefs, customs, and way of life of a group of people

• **Regions:** Places that have common (the same) characteristics

• **Environment:** Surroundings

The Lakota Indians lived in the Plains Region. They lived in homes called teepees. They were hunters and horsemen. Walking and riding horses were their main forms of transportation. The land of the Plains Region is made up of prairies, plains, and rolling hills. The region has hot summers and harsh, cold winters. The Lakota moved around the region to hunt for buffalo. They later used horses for transportation.

Contributions of American Indians

• Arts (pottery, weaving, carving) • Knowledge of the environment

• Respect for nature • Farming of corn and tobacco

Changes in American Indian culture

• American Indian cultures have changed over time.

• Today American Indians live and work in Virginia and the United States.

Learning At Home

• The Plains Region is located in the middle of our country. Work with your child to locate this region on a United States map. The land in the Plains Region is flat and has few trees. When the first Europeans arrived, the Plains were home to thousands of buffalo. The Lakota survived by hunting the buffalo which was a source of food, tools, homes, and clothing. The Lakota used buffalo hide to build teepees. The teepees could be easily taken apart and moved to follow the buffalo herds. The Lakota only killed buffalo to survive and were careful not to let any part of the animals go to waste. Work together with your child to research all the things the Lakota could make from a buffalo. Encourage your daughter or son to practice this respect for nature. Challenge your child to think of ways to keep from wasting food, clothing, and other materials in his or her life today.

• The Spanish brought the first horses to the Plains Region, and the Lakota quickly became master riders. Talk about how having horses might have changed things for the Lakota.

• American Indians are known for their pottery, weaving, and carving. Point out examples of handmade pottery and carving to your child. Show your daughter or son patterns in woven blankets and baskets. Find books in your local library that show examples of pottery, weaving, and carving. You may even decide to try your hand at one of these arts. Craft stores offer lots of materials to make learning fun!

SECOND GRADE   SOL NEWS   BULLETIN SEVEN

The Pueblo People of the Southwest

Social Studies Standards of Learning
STANDARD 2.2, 2.4

The student will compare the lives and contributions of three American Indian cultures of the past and present with emphasis on the Powhatan of the Eastern Woodlands, the Lakota of the Plains, and the Pueblo peoples of the Southwest. The student will develop map skills by:

a) Locating the United States, China, and Egypt on world maps;

c) Locating the regions of the Powhatan, Lakota, and Pueblo Indians on United States maps;

d) Understanding the relationship between the environment and the culture of the Powhatan, Lakota, and Pueblo Indians.

Essential Questions

• In what ways were past American Indian lifestyles in Virginia similar to and different from those of the Lakota and Pueblo Indians?

• What are some contributions of American Indian culture to present-day life?

• How are American Indians of the past different from those of today? Where are the regions of the Powhatan, Lakota, and Pueblo people located on a United States map?

• How did the environment affect the Powhatan, Lakota, and Pueblo Indians?

• How did the ancient Chinese, Egyptians, Powhatan, Lakota, and Pueblo people relate to their environment?

Essential Knowledge

TERMS TO KNOW

• **Culture:** The beliefs, customs, and way of life of a group of people

• **Regions:** Places that have common (the same) characteristics

• **Environment:** Surroundings

The Pueblo Indians lived in the Southwest Region. They lived in multi-story terraced buildings. They were farmers and hunters. Walking was their main forms of transportation. The land of the Southwest Region is made up of high flatlands. The Southwest Region has hot days, cold nights, and little rainfall. The Pueblo people farmed the land. They lived in villages in adobe (clay) houses.

Contributions of American Indians

• Arts (pottery, weaving, carving) • Knowledge of the environment

• Respect for nature • Farming of corn and tobacco

Changes in American Indian culture

• American Indian cultures have changed over time.

• Today, American Indians live and work in Virginia and the United States.

Learning At Home

• The Southwest Region is very dry. The days are hot and there is little rainfall. The Pueblo people adapted to this environment by building multi-storied homes on the high flatlands. Work with your child to locate the Southwest Region on a United States map.

• Discuss the difficulties of farming in a land with very little rain. Ask your child how the Pueblo peoples could provide water for their plants to grow. Why didn't they build wood and bark homes like the Powhatan Indians? Why didn't they build teepees? What made adobe homes a good choice for the Pueblo? Remind your child that all American Indians learned to use things from their environment to survive. The Southwest has few trees and few buffalo. Adobe could be made with the materials available in the region.

• Have your child reflect on all the things she or he has learned about American Indians. How were the lives of the Pueblo and Lakota different from that of the Powhatan? How were they the same? How have the lives of all American Indians changed over time? How do they live today? Remind your child that American Indians today live in communities all over Virginia and the United States.

VIRGINIA'S INDIANS

Name _____

POWHATAN INDIANS

Region	Eastern Woodlands	
Homes	Wood frame and bark houses with bark/reed coverings	
Occupation	Hunters Farmers Fishermen	
Transportation	Walked Paddled canoes	
Contributions	Arts Knowledge of the environment Respect for nature Farming of corn and tobacco	
Today	Their culture has changed over time. They live and work in Virginia and other parts of the United States.	

CAN YOU CANOE?
READER'S THEATER

Setting: Present day, traveling in a truck through the woodlands of Virginia.

Characters: A Powhatan Grandfather and his grandchild

Grandchild: I love riding in your truck, Grandfather.

Grandfather: I do too, young one.

Grandchild: The woods are very beautiful this time of year.

Grandfather: These woods were the home of our Powhatan ancestors.

Grandchild: Really? Did they have trucks too?

Grandfather: No, young one. Trucks had not yet been invented during the old times. Our ancestors walked these lands and paddled canoes on the river.

Grandchild: Where did they get canoes, Grandfather?

Grandfather: They made them from trees in the forest.

Grandchild: How did they turn a tree into a canoe?

Grandfather: They were called dugout canoes because the people would dig out one side by chopping and burning the wood.

Grandchild: That sounds like hard work.

Grandfather: It was, young one. Our people worked very hard to survive.

Grandchild: I am glad we have your truck.

Grandfather: Me too!

LAKOTA INDIANS

Name_____

LAKOTA INDIANS

Region		
Homes		
Occupation		
Transportation		
Contributions	Arts Knowledge of the environment Respect for nature	
Today	Their culture has changed over time. They live and work all over the United States.	

THE BUFFALO
READER'S THEATER

Setting: A modern day home in the Great Plains.

Characters: A Lakota Grandmother and her grandchild

Grandchild: I always have fun at your house, Grandmother.

Grandmother: I love having you here.

Grandchild: Has our family always lived in this house?

Grandmother: No, dear. Our Lakota ancestors lived on the plains. They had to follow the buffalo.

Grandchild: Why did they have to follow the buffalo?

Grandmother: There were no shopping malls long ago. The buffalo gave us all the things we needed to live.

Grandchild: Like what?

Grandmother: Our ancestors used the buffalo for food. They made their clothes from the hide of the buffalo. They even used the hide to make their homes.

Grandchild: Did they have to kill the buffalo?

Grandmother: Yes, dear. They were grateful to the buffalo for giving them the things they needed.

Grandchild: How did they kill the buffalo?

Grandmother: Long ago they had to chase the buffalo on foot to trap them in a pen. Later, they had horses to use in the hunt.

Grandchild: I am glad we can go to the grocery store.

Grandmother: Me too!

PUEBLO INDIANS

Name _____

PUEBLO INDIANS

Region		
Homes		
Occupation		
Transportation		
Contributions		
Today		

FIRST AMERICANS WORD SEARCH

Name _____

We use many American Indian words such as
PARKA and HAMMOCK when we speak.
Some of them are hidden in this puzzle?
Circle each word when you find it and then
cross it off the list. Can you find all of them?

Find:
RACCOON ~~RACCOON~~
PUMPKIN
SKUNK

CHIPMUNK
MOOSE
SQUASH
CANOE

COCOA
POTATO
SHARK
TOMATO

C	G	R	R	R	C	O	C	O	A	M
H	C	A	A	A	F	P	F	F	F	C
I	A	C	C	T	O	M	A	T	O	O
F	N	C	C	F	T	F	S	S	S	S
M	O	O	S	E	A	F	K	H	Q	Q
F	E	O	O	F	T	B	U	A	U	U
F	F	N	N	F	O	F	N	R	R	A
C	H	I	P	M	U	N	K	K	K	S
P	U	M	P	K	I	N	F	F	F	H

VOCABULARY DEFINITIONS

Key Word	Definition	Picture Clue
Adapt	To find new ways, tools, or skills to make life easier or better	
Region	A group of places that have something in common	
	Land that American Indians were forced to move to after being pushed away from their homes	
	The beliefs, customs, and way of life of a group of people	
	Places that have common (the same) characteristics	
	Surroundings	

THREE GREAT NATIONS: CUT AND SORT

Arts, knowledge of the environment, respect for nature, hunting buffalo

Their culture has changed over time. They live and work in Virginia and other parts of the U.S.A.

Their culture has changed over time. They live and work in many parts of the U.S.A.

Arts, knowledge of the environment, respect for nature, farming of corn and tobacco

Arts, knowledge of the environment, respect for nature, farming of corn and tobacco

Plains

Eastern Woodlands

Southwest

Their culture has changed over time. They live and work in many parts of the U.S.A.

THREE GREAT NATIONS

Name _____

	POWHATAN INDIANS	LAKOTA INDIANS	PUEBLO INDIANS
Region			
Homes			
Occupation			
Transportation			
Contributions			
Today			

S O L NEWS

SECOND GRADE BULLETIN EIGHT

ANCIENT EGYPT

Social Studies Standards of Learning
STANDARD 2.2, 2.4

The student will explain how the contributions of ancient China and Egypt have influenced the present world in terms of architecture, inventions, the calendar, and written language.

The student will develop map skills by:

a) Locating the United States, China, and Egypt on world maps;

b) Understanding the relationship between the environment and the culture of ancient China and Egypt;

Essential Questions

• What contributions did the people of ancient China and Egypt make to the development of written language?

• What inventions came from ancient China and Egypt?

• What examples of architecture from ancient China and Egypt are still present today?

• Where are the United States, China, and Egypt located on a world map?

• How did the environment affect the culture of Egypt and China?

• How did the ancient Chinese, Egyptians, Powhatan, Lakota, and Pueblo people relate to their environment?

Essential Knowledge

TERMS TO KNOW

• **Ancient:** Long, long ago

• **Architecture**: The design of buildings

• **Contribution**: The act of giving or doing something

Egypt is located on the continent of Africa. They developed a written language known as hieroglyphics. The contributions of ancient Egypt include the inventions of paper made from papyrus, a 365-day calendar, and the clock.

The pyramids are another contribution of this ancient culture, which can still be seen today. Many inventions of ancient China and Egypt are still used today.

Egypt is known for its vast desert. Most of the people of ancient Egypt lived in the Nile River Valley. At that time the Nile River flooded each year, making the Nile River Valley a good place for growing crops. The ancient Egyptians farmed and irrigated the land near the Nile River. The climate of Egypt is hot and dry.

Learning At Home

• Ancient Egypt is a fascinating topic for second grade students. You will find many books on the subject at your local library. There are also many resources available on the Internet. Please remember to preview and bookmark any web-based resources you want to use at home.

• Talk with your child about how we have learned about ancient cultures. Explain the role of the archeologist. Read about the discovery of King Tut's tomb by archaeologist Howard Carter. **Tut's Mummy Lost...And Found,** by Judy Donnelly, is a book your family may enjoy.

• Take some time to research hieroglyphics. Work together as a family to write your names using this ancient form of writing.

• Help your child understand the term "architecture" by looking at various buildings in your community. How are they different? How are they the same? Look through magazines and cut out pictures of various types of architecture. Look for apartments, homes, castles, banks, skyscrapers, and other buildings. Glue them on poster board to create an architectural collage.

• Build your own pyramid using cardboard, sugar cubes, or building blocks. Look for examples of this form of architecture in your community and in pictures. Start with the back of a one dollar bill.

• Sundials are one way of telling time. Look for sundials in your community. Talk with your child and try to come up with a way to build one at home.

• The Virginia Museum of Fine Arts in Richmond has some examples of Egyptian art. You may want to plan a family field trip to this great museum.

S O L NEWS

ANCIENT CHINA

Social Studies Standards of Learning
STANDARD 2.2, 2.4

The student will explain how the contributions of ancient China and Egypt have influenced the present world in terms of architecture, inventions, the calendar, and written language. The student will develop map skills by:

a) Locating the United States, China, and Egypt on world maps;

b) Understanding the relationship between the environment and the culture of ancient China and Egypt;

Essential Questions

• What contributions did the people of ancient China and Egypt make to the development of written language?

• What inventions came from ancient China and Egypt?

• What examples of architecture from ancient China and Egypt are still present today?

• Where are the United States, China, and Egypt located on a world map?

• How did the environment affect the culture of Egypt and China?

• How did the ancient Chinese, Egyptians, Powhatan, Lakota, and Pueblo people relate to their environment?

Essential Knowledge

TERMS TO KNOW

• **Ancient:** Long, long ago

• **Architecture**: The design of buildings

• **Contribution**: The act of giving or doing something

China is located on the continent of Asia. The contributions of ancient China include the inventions of the kite, silk cloth, the compass, bronze, and fireworks. The Great Wall is another contribution of this ancient culture, which can still be seen today.

Many inventions of ancient China and Egypt are still used today.

China has four seasons. The land in China has forests, hills, mountains, and deserts. The ancient Chinese settled along the Huang He. They fished, farmed, and irrigated the land.

Learning At Home

• You can explore some of the contributions of ancient China by visiting a local mall with your family.
Visit a sporting goods store to look at modern examples of a compass. How is it used to show the cardinal directions? Look for examples of various kites. The ancient Chinese did not use kites for fun. Kites were used as signals to measure distances and to scare away enemies. They were even used to catch fish.

• As you walk through a clothing store, point out items made with silk. How is it used? Talk about the differences between silk and other fabrics.

• Look in hardware stores to find objects made of bronze. Bronze is a metal which is made by combining copper and tin. It is known for the rich, dark color it acquires over time. Bronze is used to make statues and is often found in gears, valves, and various plumbing fixtures.

• End the day with a visit to a Chinese restaurant to sample new foods. Try out some chopsticks just for fun!

• Celebrate Chinese culture in your home by checking out some of these books from your local library.

Grandfather Tang's Story, by Ann Tompert and Robert Andrew Parker, is a Chinese folktale told with the use of tangrams. Have fun working these ancient Chinese puzzles with your child.

Lion Dancer: Ernie Wan's Chinese New Year, by Kate Waters and Martha Cooper, is the story of the celebration of Chinese New Year in New York City. It showcases the value of diversity in America.

Lóng is a Dragon: Chinese Writing for Children, by Peggy Goldstein, is filled with examples of how to draw Chinese characters. Provide paper and pen and allow your child to practice making the symbols.

ANCIENT EGYPT

Name_____

ANCIENT EGYPT

Continent		
Important River		
Architecture		
Written Language		
Inventions		

ANCIENT EGYPT TREASURE MAP

Name _____

MATERIALS:

Scrap paper, crayons, liquid glue, blue yarn, and some sand.

1. Draw a compass rose in the blank square on the world map.

2. Find the location of Egypt on the world map. Place a drop of glue on the spot. Sprinkle a little sand on the drop of glue. Lift your paper and shake the excess off onto the scrap paper.

3. On the big map of Egypt, find the Nile River. Use glue to draw over the line of the Nile River. Place the blue yarn over the glue.

4. Use a black crayon to draw a line right next to the Nile River, from the top all the way to the bottom. Draw the line on both sides of the river. This is where you would find the dark, rich soil of the Nile River Valley. This is where the Egyptians can grow their food.

5. The rest of Egypt is desert. Place a small amount of liquid glue on the rest of the land of Egypt. Spread thinly. Sprinkle the glue with sand and then shake the excess off onto the scrap paper. This is the Egyptian desert.

6. Create a map legend for the map of Egypt.

WORLD MAP

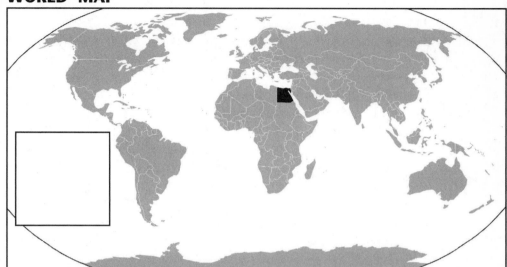

EGYPT MAP

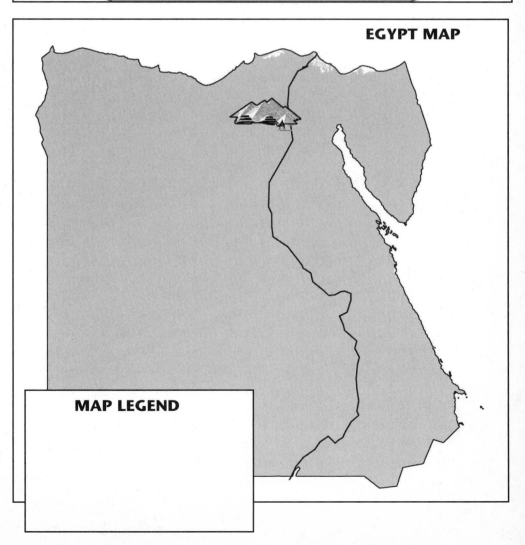

MAP LEGEND

INSIDE THE MUMMY'S TOMB

Name _____

Can you read this?

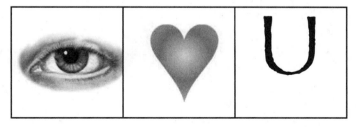

When people in Egypt first started writing, they used pictures to tell their story. Over time, certain pictures started being used as letters. Look at these **hieroglyphics** *(hi-row-gliff-iks)* and see if you can tell how the mummy feels today.

Challenge: Use these hieroglyphics to create more words. How many can you make?

BUILD A PYRAMID

1. Read the sentences on each side of the pyramid. Draw pictures to go with each sentence below it in the space provided.

2. On the base of the pyramid, draw a mummy.

3. Use your scissors to carefully cut out the template. Cut only on the solid lines.

4. Gently fold the paper on the dotted lines.

5. Flip the template over to the blank side.

6. Draw lines and make the building blocks that were used to build the pyramids.

7. Fold the tab marked "Tab-Glue."

8. With the building blocks on the outside, fold on all the other dotted lines to make the pyramid.

9. Use your glue stick to put glue over the words "Tab-Glue" to make the sides of the pyramid.

10. Fold the tab marked "Tab-Tuck in" to complete the pyramid.

Tab - Glue

Papyrus grew on the banks of the Nile River.

They created a calendar based on the sun.

Their leader was called a pharaoh.

Egyptians used a written language called hieroglypics.

Draw a picture of a mummy here.

Tab - Tuck in

WRITE LIKE AN EGYPTIAN
READER'S THEATER

Setting: A modern day school

Characters: A second grader and an archaeologist

Student: I have always wanted to meet an archaeologist. What do you do?

Archaeologist: I study ancient people and their cultures.

Student: Our class learned about ancient Egypt. Have you studied their culture?

Archaeologist: Yes!

Student: How do you learn about things that happened so long ago?

Archaeologist: We learn about life in ancient times by studying the things that ancient people left behind. The ancient Egyptians had a written language. By learning to read their hieroglyphics, we can learn about their life.

Student: Where do you find hieroglyphics?

Archaeologist: We find them on ancient tombs and monuments. We also find them on papyrus.

Student: What is papyrus?

Archaeologist: Papyrus is similar to paper but it is made from the papyrus plant. Stems from the plant were flattened, dried, and stuck together to make pages. Scribes used ink and sharpened reeds to write on the papyrus. Where do you think the ancient Egyptians got the papyrus plants?

Student: Hmmm…..in class we learned that the Nile River Valley was a good place to grow things. Did they grow papyrus there?

Archaeologist: It sounds like you learned a great deal about ancient Egypt!

IS THAT A MUMMY?

Name _____

Ancient Egyptians believed that people could live another life after they died. They thought this would happen if the body of the dead person was **mummified**.

Mummification was a complicated process that took 70 days. First, the body was dried using a special salt called natron. Next, the body was wrapped in strips of cloth. Finally, the body was placed in a coffin. The coffins were made of wood or stone. The decorated coffin was called a **sarcophagus**.

Describe the process of mummification.

First,_____

_____

_____

Next,_____

_____

_____

Finally,_____

_____

_____

Challenge: Who was King Tut? Why is he so famous? Learn more about this famous pharaoh!

ANCIENT CHINA

Name _____

ANCIENT CHINA

Continent		
Important River		
Architecture		
Written Language		
Inventions		

ANCIENT CHINA TREASURE MAP

Name_____

You will need: Scrap paper, crayons, liquid glue, blue yarn, and glitter.

1. Draw a compass rose on the world map.

2. Find China on the world map. Place one drop of glue on the spot. Sprinkle a little glitter on the drop of glue. Lift your paper and shake the excess glitter off onto the scrap paper. Do you know why we are using glitter? What did the Chinese invent that looks like glitter in the night sky?

3. On the large map of China, find the Huang He. Use the glue to draw over the line of the river. Place the blue yarn over the glue.

4. Use a black crayon to draw a line right next to the Huang He. Draw the line on both sides of the river. This is where the ancient Chinese settled. They fished, farmed, and irrigated the land.

5. Find the Great Wall. Use liquid glue to draw over the line showing the Great Wall. Place the small pieces of elbow macaroni along this line. Have the macaroni standing on the ends so that it forms a wall that divides part of the country.

6. Create a map legend for the map of China.

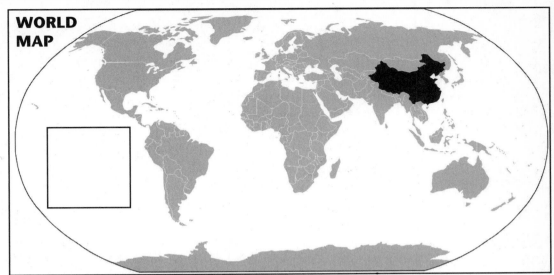

WORLD MAP

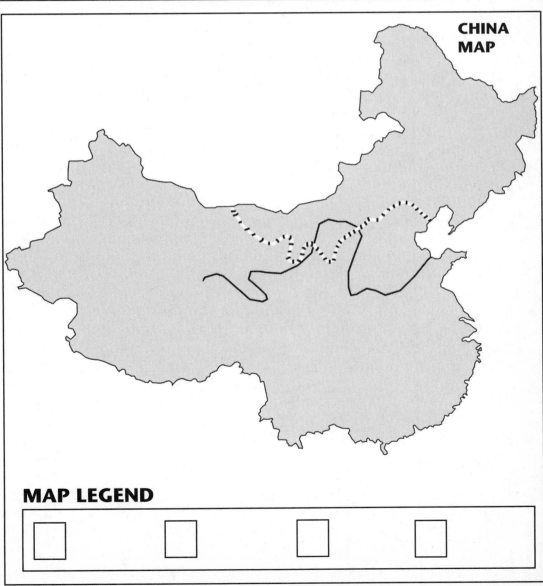

CHINA MAP

MAP LEGEND

☐   ☐   ☐   ☐

谢 谢 XIE-XIE*

Extra Enrichment

Do you know what xie-xie means? Can you guess how to say it? Learn to count to ten and say a few words, just in case you end up at the Great Wall of China!

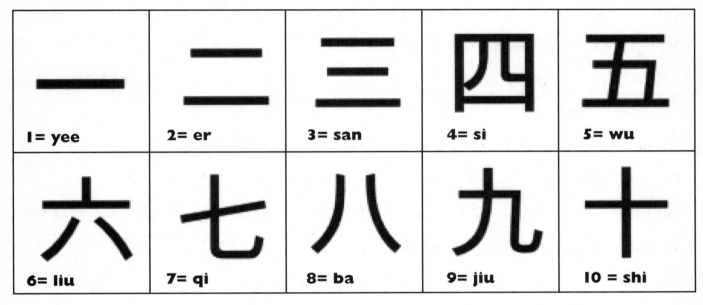

1 = yee 2 = er 3 = san 4 = si 5 = wu

6 = liu 7 = qi 8 = ba 9 = jiu 10 = shi

Now answer the following questions in Chinese. Try to write your answers in Chinese numbers.

How old are you? _____

How much is 四 plus 五 ? _____

How much is 八 minus 六 ? _____

SUPER CHALLENGE:

If Sally has 三 cookies and Carmen has 七 cookies, but Bob eats 四, how many cookies are left?

* XIE-XIE means thank you. It is pronounced *zhee-zhee*. Here are a few more words to know.

HELLO - Ni hao

HOW OLD ARE YOU - Ni ji sui?

I AM ____ YEARS OLD - Wo _____ Sui

GOODBYE - Zai Jian

CLEVER CHINESE CONTRIBUTIONS

READER'S THEATER

Setting: A second grade classroom   Characters: A teacher and six students

Teacher: Your homework assignment was to search your home to find something   that was invented in ancient China. What did you find?

Student One: I found a compass! My family used it when we went hiking. My mom said it kept us from getting lost.

Student Two: This is my kite. The ancient Chinese used kites to measure distances. I just use mine to have fun!

Student Three: My dad found this silk tie in his closet.

Student Four: Hey! I brought in my mom's silk blouse. It is so soft.

Student Five: We went to see the fireworks on the Fourth of July. This is a picture of what we saw. They were really loud!

Student Six: My grandfather let me bring his bronze medal. He won it when he was young. He was a fast runner then!

Teacher: I am so proud of you all! You did a great job finding examples of the contributions of ancient China!

VOCABULARY DEFINITIONS

Key Word	Definition	Picture Clue
	A long time ago	
	A group of countries ruled over by a single nation	
	The design of buildings	
	The act of giving or doing something	
	People that have a strong government as well as art, music, writing, and more	

CONCEPT OF DEFINITION

Name _____

What is it?

What is it like?

What are some examples?

What is it?

What is it like?

What are some examples?

CONCEPT OF DEFINITION

Name_____

What is it?

What is it like?

What are some examples?

- -

What is it?

What is it like?

What are some examples?

CONCEPT OF DEFINITION

Name _____

What is it?

What is it like?

What are some examples?

What is it?

What is it like?

What are some examples?

KNOW IT? DRAW IT! SORT IT!

Directions: *Read the words in the boxes below. Draw a picture in each box to help you remember the word. Cut the boxes apart. Sort the words into an ancient Egypt pile and ancient China pile.*

Huang He	Hieroglyphics	Kites	Water Clock
Compass	Characters	Calendar	Great Wall
Bronze	Silk	Fireworks	Papyrus
Asia	Africa	Nile	Pyramids

SECOND GRADE

S O L
NEWS
BULLETIN TEN

GEOGRAPHY

Social Studies Standards of Learning
STANDARD 2.4

The student will develop map skills by :
a) Locating the United States, China, and Egypt on world maps
b) Understanding the relationship between the environment and the culture of ancient China and Egypt
c) Locating the regions of the Powhatan, Lakota, and Pueblo Indians on United States maps
d) Understanding the relationship between the environment and the culture of the Powhatan, Lakota, and Pueblo Indians

Essential Questions

• Where are the United States, China, and Egypt located on a world map?
• Where are the regions of the Powhatan, Lakota, and Pueblo people located on a United States map?
• How did the environment affect the Powhatan, Lakota, and Pueblo Indians?
• How did the environment affect the culture of Egypt and China?
• How did the ancient Chinese, Egyptians, Powhatan, Lakota, and Pueblo people relate to their environment?

Essential Knowledge
TERMS TO KNOW
• **Climate:** The kind of weather an area has over a long period of time
• **Land:** The solid surface of the Earth
• **Environment:** Surroundings
China is located in Asia. Egypt is located in Africa. The United States is located in North America.

(continued on the reverse side)

Learning At Home
Where a civilization develops affects the way that civilization develops.

• Have your child practice using a map and a globe to locate the various cultures we have studied. Ask him or her to describe what life would be like in each place.

• People who live in hot, dry climates depend on rivers. Rivers provide water for animals and people to drink. They allow people the opportunity to irrigate the land to grow crops. Rivers provide water for cooking, cleaning, and building. Ancient peoples adapted to their environments to develop ways to build homes and provide food for their families. They built their homes with materials that were available in their environment. They learned to use native plants and animals as food.

Talk with your child about foods grown or found in Virginia. If possible, try to spend a few days eating only foods locally grown or raised in a 100-mile radius from your home.

• Irrigation was important to the people of ancient Egypt and China. Talk about the process with your child. Where does the water come from? How do the people get the water to the plants?

The people of Egypt got their water from the Nile River, which flooded each year, bringing much-needed water and rich soil to the Nile River Valley. The ancient Egyptians developed the 365-day calendar to help them predict the flooding of the Nile.

In China, people also depended on irrigation to grow crops such as rice. Even today we try to find ways to bring water to farms and gardens during periods of dry weather. Research the ancient methods of irrigation and point out examples of irrigation systems in your community today.

(continued on the reverse side)

Essential Knowledge
(CONTINUED)

• The ancient Chinese settled along the Huang He. They fished, farmed, and irrigated the land.
• The ancient Egyptians farmed and irrigated the land near the Nile River.
• The Powhatan farmed, fished, hunted, used trees for homes and canoes, and gathered plants for food.
• The Lakota moved around the region to hunt for buffalo. They later used horses for transportation.
• The Pueblo people farmed the land. They lived in villages in adobe (clay) houses.

	CLIMATE	LAND
China	Seasons	Forests, hills, mountains, deserts
Egypt	Hot, dry	Nile River Valley, deserts, flooding
Eastern Woodlands (Powhatan)	Mild winters Hot, humid summers	Rivers, hills, mountains, coastline
Plains (Lakota)	Hot summers Harsh, cold winters	Plains, prairies, rolling hills
Southwest (Pueblo people)	Hot days; Cold nights; Little rainfall	High flatlands

Learning At Home
(CONTINUED)

• We adapt to the changing seasons by changing our activities and our clothing. When we travel to different places, we adapt to the climate by packing appropriate items in our suitcases.

Have your child pretend he or she is packing to travel to each of the regions we have studied. Each region is different. Talk about what you would need to survive in each place. What type of clothing would you need? Think about the climate and the terrain and the time of year you are traveling. What type of shoes would you need? Talk about the things you would see and the food you would eat. Have fun planning your make-believe trips.

• Plan a family outing to the mountains, the coast, or the river. Ask your child to describe the surroundings. Talk about the different things you can do in each environment. Encourage your child to notice different types of transportation. Use maps to plan your trip!

• Listen to the weather forecast each evening. Use this opportunity to talk about the forecast and the appropriate clothes to wear to adapt to the weather.

• Use an outdoor thermometer to teach your child how to read the temperature. Help him or her begin to understand how the number of degrees relates to the amount of warmth.
Use a calendar to record the type of weather that occurs each day for two weeks. Work with your child to create a graph of the information.

LANDFORMS PICTURE DICTIONARY

NAME _____

Coastland	**Desert**
Forest	**High flatland**
Hills	**Mountains**
Plains	**Prairie**
River	**River Valley**

A DAY IN THE DESERT

China, Egypt, and the United States all have deserts.
Here are some "cool" facts about these hot places.

1. Most deserts are very hot during the day. It can reach 136 degrees Farenheit!
But heat is not what makes a place a desert since deserts can get very cold at night.
Lack of rain is what makes a desert special.

2. The Sahara gets less than three inches of rain a year. In some parts it does not rain
for years. Compare that with Virginia's average rainfall of about 40 inches a year.

3. Deserts are not just made of sand. Most deserts are rock and dirt.

4. Egypt is in the SAHARA, which is the world's biggest desert. It is in Africa.

5. The GOBI is the next biggest desert. It is in China on the continent of Asia.

6. The SONORA desert is in North America. The Pueblo Indians live near this desert.

Color in each of these three deserts. Can you tell which each is?
Write the name of each desert in the spaces below.

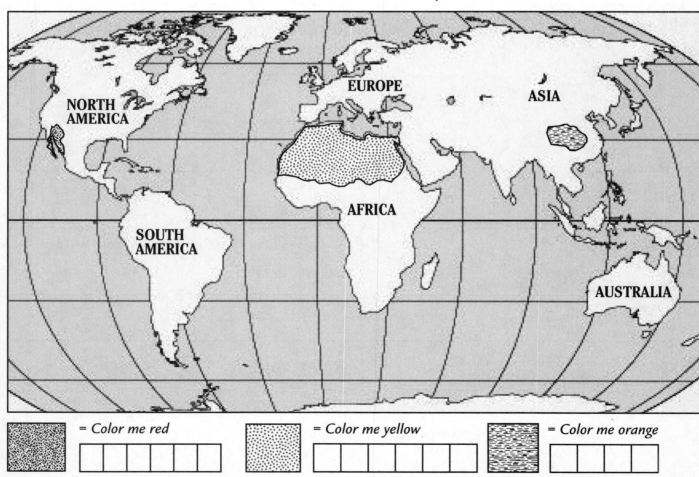

| = Color me red | = Color me yellow | = Color me orange |

ADAPTING TO THE ENVIRONMENT
Relationship Map

People

LAND

+

CLIMATE

RELATIONSHIP

The land and the climate make up the environment of a region.

How did the environment affect the people and their culture?
How did the people relate to the environment?

ADAPTING TO THE ENVIRONMENT
Relationship Map

People

LAND

+

CLIMATE

RELATIONSHIP

The land and the climate make up the environment of a region.

How did the environment affect the people and their culture?
How did the people relate to the environment?

ADAPTING TO THE ENVIRONMENT

Relationship Map

People

RELATIONSHIP

LAND

+

CLIMATE

The land and the climate make up the environment of a region.

How did the environment affect the people and their culture?
How did the people relate to the environment?

SURVIVAL GUIDE

This guide will help you plan for your survival in many different environments. On each page you will find yourself in a different place. You must use what you can find around you to survive. There are no stores, no electricity, no telephone, no machinery, and no cars. You must depend on your knowledge to build a life.

WHAT WILL YOU DO?

You are in a place with flat land that is covered with tall grass. Many large buffalo are grazing on the flat grassy land. The summers are very hot, but the winters are harsh and very cold. What will you do?

WHAT WILL YOU DO?

You are in a place with many trees. There are mountains, hills, and rivers nearby. You can even walk to the coastline and see the ocean. The winters are mild, but the summers are hot and humid. How will you survive?

WHAT WILL YOU DO?

You are surrounded by high flatlands. The days are hot, and the nights are cold. There is very little rain. What will you do to survive?

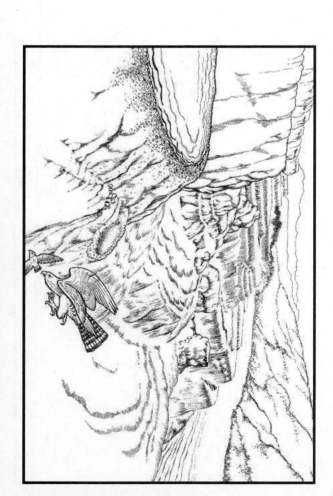

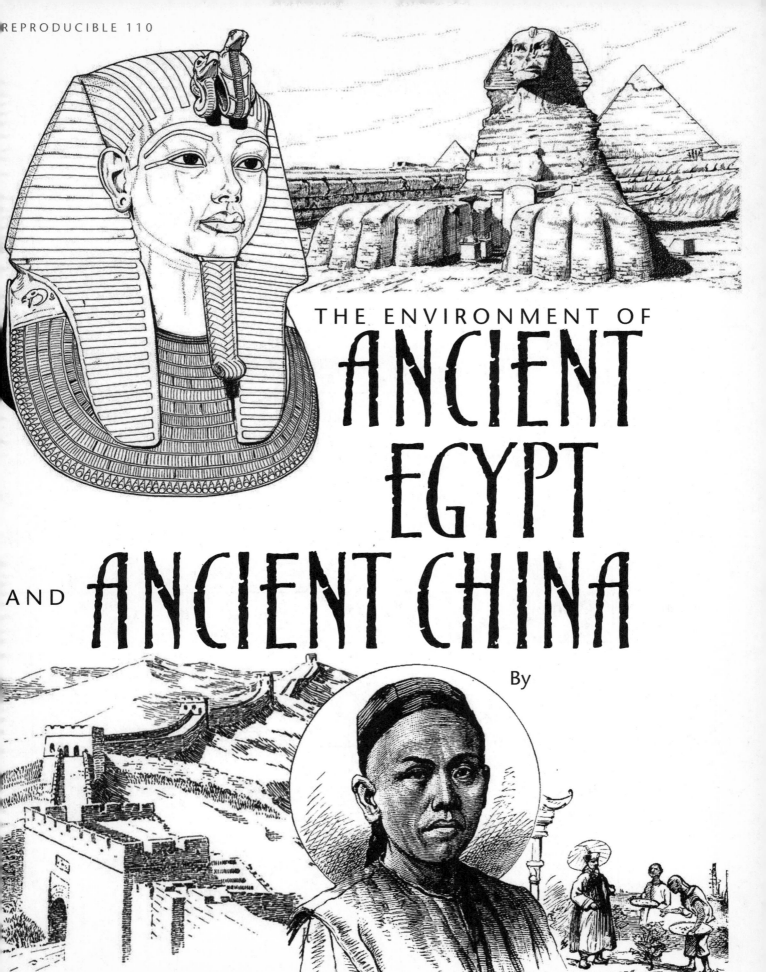

THE ENVIRONMENT OF
ANCIENT EGYPT
AND ANCIENT CHINA

By

CHINA'S CLIMATE AND LAND

Use a red crayon or marker to color in where China is located on a world map. →

This is what the land looks like in China. →

The climate in China is

_____

_____

One major river located in China is the _____

Describe how the Chinese related to their environment. You may use both words and pictures.

EGYPT'S CLIMATE AND LAND

Use a yellow crayon or marker to color in where Egypt is located on a world map. ⟶

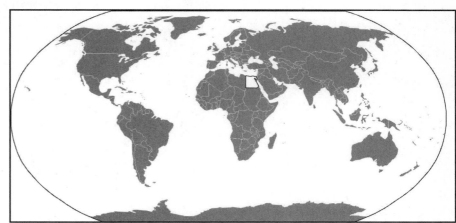

This is what the land looks like in Egypt. ⟶

The climate in Egypt is

_____

_____

One major river located in Egypt is the _____

In the space below, describe how the Egyptians related to their environment. You may use both words and pictures.

THE POWHATAN, LAKOTA, AND PUEBLO PEOPLE

THEIR ENVIRONMENT AND CULTURE

WRITTEN BY

THE EASTERN WOODLAND INDIANS

This is the region where the Eastern Woodland people lived in North America. The Powhatan were a part of this group.

⟶

This is what the land looks like in the Eastern Woodlands.

⟶

The climate in Eastern Woodlands is

_____

_____

In the space below, describe how the Powhatan related to their environment. You may use both words and pictures.

THE LAKOTA

This is where the Lakota
people lived in North America.

⟶

This is what the land looks
like in the Plains. ⟶

The climate in the Plains is

_____

_____

In the space below, describe how the Lakota related to their environment.
You may use both words and pictures.

THE PUEBLO

This is where the Pueblo people lived in North America. ⟶

This is what the land looks like in the Southwest. ⟶

The climate in the Southwest is

_____

_____

In the space below, describe how the Pueblo related to their environment. You may use both words and pictures.

VOCABULARY DEFINITIONS

Key Word	Definition	Picture Clue
	The study of the Earth's surface—its land, people and climate	
	The kind of weather an area has over a long period of time	
	The solid surface of the Earth	
	To bring water for crops from somewhere else	

S O L NEWS

CHANGING TIMES

Social Studies Standards of Learning
STANDARD 2.3

The student will identify and compare changes in community life over time in terms of buildings, jobs, transportation, and population.

Essential Question
• How and why have communities changed over time?

Essential Knowledge
TERMS TO KNOW
• **Community:** A place where people live, work, and play
• **Population:** The number of people living in a community
• **Transportation:** A way of moving people and things from one place to another

The way people live today is different from the way people lived long ago.

New inventions have led to changes in buildings, jobs, transportation, and populations of communities over time.

Learning At Home

• Grandparents can be a great source of help in explaining how life has changed over time. During your next visit, ask them to tell your child about their young years. Have them describe the community they lived in and how it has changed over time. Ask them how they traveled and talk about their first jobs. Encourage them to show pictures of the way they dressed or their first car. What was their favorite music? Perhaps they still have some of their old toys. Talk to your child about life before computers, cell phones, and video games.

• Plan a family trip to a museum or antique store to see objects from the past. Look for vintage clothing, kitchen tools, and toys. Talk about how people in the past often made their own butter and raised hens to have fresh eggs. Bake something completely from scratch.

• As you travel around your community, look for historic homes and buildings. Compare them to modern buildings.

• Rent an old movie or TV show from the past. Challenge your child to notice the differences in clothing and transportation. What types of jobs does your child see? Are the occupations different from today's? How?

• Talk about what it means to "invent" something new. Give examples of some of the new inventions you have seen in your lifetime.

• Visit a museum home in your area or take a family field trip to places such as Colonial Williamsburg, Monticello, Mount Vernon, or the Maggie Walker House in Richmond. Mount Vernon and Monticello were not typical homes for their time, but they do show how basic chores such as cooking and farming were done in the past.

• Look for opportunities in your community to have your child experience various types of transportation. What fun it would be to take a horse drawn wagon or ride the train to visit a friend!

WHAT CAME FIRST?

Name _____

Directions: *Draw a picture of yourself and write the date of your birth in the first box. Cut apart the cards. Think about them carefully. Which one do you think came first? Sort them in order from first to last to make a timeline. When you have finished your sort, wait for your teacher's instructions.*

I was born in _____

Skateboard

Airplane

iPod

Internet

Car

Television

Light bulbs

HOW HAS LIFE CHANGED?

Draw pictures to show the differences between life 100 years ago and life today for each catagory listed.

	Community *A place where people live, work, and play*	**Population** *The number of people in a community*	**Transportation** *A way to move people and things*
100 years ago			
Today			

WANT TO BUY A CAR? Name _____

CAR SALES IN AMERICA 1900-2000

10 million				
6 million				
2 million				
0	**Before 1900**	**1925**	**1950**	**2000**

In 1889 inventors began experimenting with gasoline engines. Until 1900 there were very few cars. Most people walked, rode horses, or traveled in horse-pulled carriages. Cars were not made in quantity until 1901. *Use this blank graph to add the following facts. Use crayons to color in the columns.*

Two million cars were sold in 1925 • Six million cars were sold in 1950
In 2000, ten million cars were sold

1 How has the number of cars changed over time?

_____

2 In 1900 most of the roads in America were made of dirt. What are most roads made of today?

_____

3 How do you think the use of the car has changed America?

_____

WHERE THE BUFFALO ROAM

Name _____

POPULATION OF BUFFALO FROM 1600-2000

1. How many buffalo were living on the Plains in the 1700s?

_____

2. How many buffalo lived on the Plains in 1800s _____

3. What has happened to the number of buffalo over time?

_____

4. Why do you think this has happened?

_____

_____

Challenge: On the back of this paper write a number sentence to show the difference between the number of buffalo in 1700 and the number in 1900.

_____

TEST TAKING STRATEGY 7

Name _____

Maps, Charts, and Pictures

Continents and Oceans

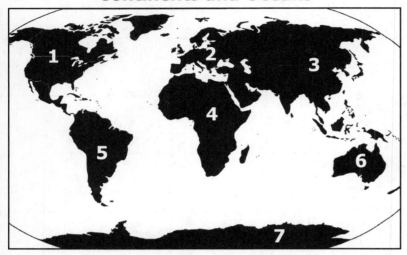

1 According to the map, the number 3 represents which continent?

A China

B Europe

C Richmond

D Asia

2 According to the pie chart, which form of transportation is most used in the United States today?

F horse

G car

H train

J jet

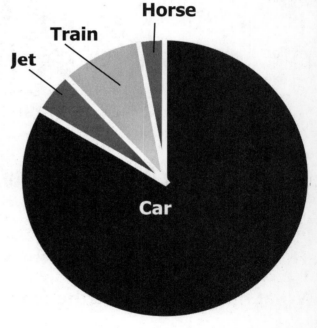

3 Which picture shows how people lived a long time ago?

A 1

B 2

C 3

D 4

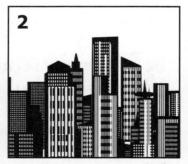

VOCABULARY DEFINITIONS

Name _____

Key Word	Definition	Picture Clue
	A place where people live, work, and play	
	The number of people living in a community	
	A way of moving people and things from one place to another	

SOL NEWS

AMERICAN HEROES

Social Studies Standards of Learning
STANDARD 2.11

The student will identify George Washington, Abraham Lincoln, Susan B. Anthony, Helen Keller, Jackie Robinson, and Martin Luther King, Jr. as Americans whose contributions improved the lives of other Americans.

Essential Questions

• How did George Washington, Abraham Lincoln, Susan B. Anthony, Helen Keller, Jackie Robinson, and Martin Luther King, Jr. help to improve the lives of other Americans?

Essential Knowledge

Famous Americans and their contributions:

• **George Washington**: He led the fight for freedom from England and helped establish a new country.

• **Abraham Lincoln:** He was the President of the United States who helped free African American slaves.

• **Susan B. Anthony:** She led the struggle to give women equal rights, including the right to vote.

• **Helen Keller:** She overcame disabilities and worked to help others who were blind and deaf.

• **Jackie Robinson:** He was the first African American player in the major leagues of baseball. His actions helped to bring about other opportunities for African Americans.

• **Martin Luther King, Jr.:** He was an African American minister who worked so that all people would be treated fairly. He led peaceful marches and gave speeches.

Learning At Home

• All of the famous Americans we study in second grade worked to improve the lives of all Americans. George Washington led the fight for freedom from English rule. Abraham Lincoln worked to end slavery. Susan B. Anthony, Helen Keller, Jackie Robinson, and Martin Luther King, Jr. worked for equal rights for all people.

• George Washington (1732-1799) and Abraham Lincoln (1809-1865) are two of our most famous presidents. We see their pictures each day on our coins and paper money. If possible, plan a trip to Washington, D.C. to see the Washington Monument, the Lincoln Memorial, and Washington's home at Mount Vernon.

• Much of the early history of our country took place in Virginia. Visit nearby Revolutionary or Civil War sites and discuss our reasons for fighting. Talk with your child about George Washington and the events leading up to the Revolutionary War. Reflect on the bravery of the men who signed the Declaration of Independence, the fight for freedom, and the founding of a new country.

What Are We Learning?

Even after the Revolutionary War, not everyone in the new country was free. Many African Americans were enslaved. Talk with your child about the meaning of slavery. Ask him or her to imagine a life with no hope for a better future—a life of working day in and day out for no money.

Your child is learning that Abraham Lincoln helped our country through very difficult times. He is known for his leadership during the Civil War and for freeing the slaves.

Votes for Women!

After the Civil War, many people of color and most women were denied the right to vote. Voting was reserved for white males. Women could not vote, own property, or hold certain jobs.

We are learning about Susan B. Anthony (1820-1906). She spent her life working to end slavery but is most famous for her leadership in seeking the right for women to vote. Although she died before realizing her dream, the **19th Amendment to the U.S. Constitution**—known as the Susan B. Anthony amendment—was passed in 1920. Women could finally vote! Discuss the fact that even though half the population is female, it took many years to change the unfair laws.

Nothing Could Stop Her

Students are fascinated with the story of Helen Keller (1880-1968), who is a wonderful example for us all. She lost her hearing and sight at a very young age, but with the help of her teacher, Anne Sullivan, Keller became the first deaf and blind person to earn a college degree. Keller went on to become an advocate for people with disabilities. She also wrote twelve books and visited countries around the world.

Learn more about this remarkable woman at the website of the American Federation of the Blind. There is a special link for children called **Braille Bug**. Your child might enjoy *A Girl Named Helen Keller,* by Margo Lundell, available at your local library.

Talk with your child about the difficulties Helen Keller had to overcome and the impact of her success.

Breaking the Color Barrier

Life in America in 1947 was different from life today. In many parts of the country, African Americans and whites ate in separate restaurants, sat in separate locations on buses, drank from separate water fountains, lived in separate neighborhoods, and went to separate schools. African Americans were denied jobs and opportunities. Jackie Robinson's bravery opened the door so that our society could begin to appreciate all of its citizens.

Jackie Robinson (1919-1972) lived an honorable life during a very difficult time. Learn more by visiting the Baseball Hall of Fame website. Robinson lived his life by nine principles: courage, determination, teamwork, persistence, integrity, citizenship, justice, commitment, and excellence. Talk about these values with your child. Why are they important? How can we display them in our lives? Ask your child about the difficulties Robinson faced as the first African American player on a major league baseball team. How did his principles help him cope?

Dr. Martin Luther King, Jr. (1929-1968) dreamed that people of all colors would learn to live in harmony. He led non-violent protests against unfair laws. He was never elected President of the United States and never served in the government. Yet every year, in January, our country celebrates Martin Luther King, Jr. Day to honor this remarkable man.

Various websites offer video of Dr. King's 1963 "I Have a Dream" address, delivered at the March on Washington. Watch this with your child. Talk about the power of his words and the importance of judging people by "the content of their character."

Martin Luther King, Jr. once said, "Life's most urgent question is: what are you doing for others?" What did Dr. King do for others? Did he make life better for other Americans? How can we work together to continue to fulfill his dreams?

Name _____

GEORGE WASHINGTON

George Washington is known as the "Father of Our Country."

George Washington was the first President of the United States.

George Washington led the fight for freedom from England.

George Washington helped to establish a new country.

Name _____

AN INTERVIEW WITH...

Write a script for a two-person play. Pretend you are a news reporter and you are interviewing a famous American. Fill in the blanks and perform with a friend.

Reporter: **Hello! My name is** _____

and I am here today with _____.

You all know _____**is**

very famous for _____.

Please tell us where were you born?

Famous American: _____

Reporter: **What was life in our country like when you were young?**

Famous American: _____

_____

_____

Reporter: **Tell us some of the things you did in your life.**

Famous American: _____

_____

_____

Reporter: **You did so many things. Which one do you think was most**

important?

Famous American: _____

_____

Reporter: **Thank you for your time** _____.

_____

Name _____

AN INTERVIEW WITH...

Write a script for a two-person play. Pretend you are a news reporter and you are interviewing a famous American. Fill in the blanks and perform with a friend.

Reporter: **Hello! My name is** _____

and I am here today with _____.

You all know _____**is**

very famous for _____.

Please tell us where were you born?

Famous American: _____

Reporter: **What was life in our country like when you were young?**

Famous American: _____

_____

_____

Reporter: **Tell us some of the things you did in your life.**

Famous American: _____

_____

_____

Reporter: **You did so many things. Which one do you think was most**

important?

Famous American: _____

_____

Reporter: **Thank you for your time** _____.

_____

Name _____

AN INTERVIEW WITH...

Write a script for a two-person play. Pretend you are a news reporter and you are interviewing a famous American. Fill in the blanks and perform with a friend.

Reporter: Hello! My name is _____

and I am here today with _____.

You all know _____ is

very famous for _____.

Please tell us where were you born?

Famous American: _____

Reporter: What was life in our country like when you were young?

Famous American: _____

_____

_____

Reporter: Tell us some of the things you did in your life.

Famous American: _____

_____

_____

Reporter: You did so many things. Which one do you think was most important?

Famous American: _____

_____

Reporter: Thank you for your time _____.

_____

Name _____

AN INTERVIEW WITH...

Write a script for a two-person play. Pretend you are a news reporter and you are interviewing a famous American. Fill in the blanks and perform with a friend.

Reporter: **Hello! My name is** _____

and I am here today with _____.

You all know _____ **is**

very famous for _____.

Please tell us where were you born?

Famous American: _____

Reporter: **What was life in our country like when you were young?**

Famous American: _____

_____

_____

Reporter: **Tell us some of the things you did in your life.**

Famous American: _____

_____

_____

Reporter: **You did so many things. Which one do you think was most**

important?

Famous American: _____

_____

Reporter: **Thank you for your time** _____.

_____

HELEN KELLER

Helen Keller was blind and deaf.

Helen Keller overcame her diabilities.

Helen Keller worked to help others who were blind and/or deaf.

Name _____

JACKIE ROBINSON

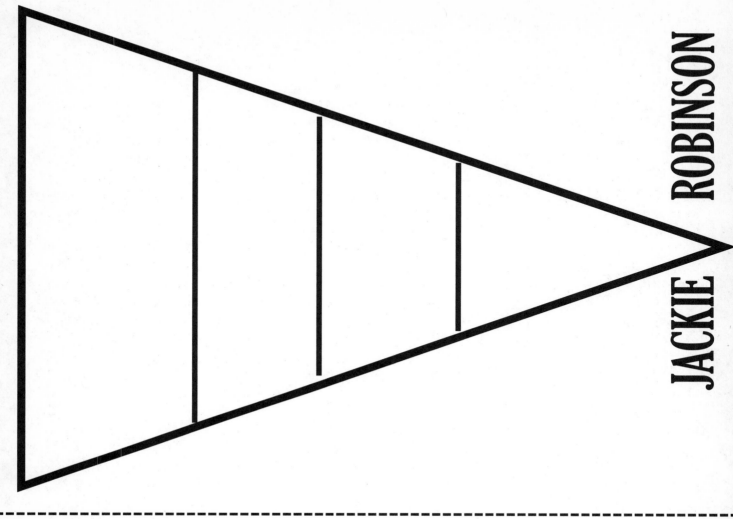

Jackie Robinson was the first African American player in the major leagues of baseball.

Jackie Robinson's actions helped to bring about other opportunities for African Americans.

Name _____

MARTIN LUTHER KING, JR.

AMERICAN HERO AWARD

In this chapter you have learned about six great American leaders. Pretend that you have been given the power to present an American Hero Award to one of these people. Which person would you select? What did this person do to improve the lives of other Americans? Write a speech about the person you have chosen and his or her contribution to our country.

VOCABULARY DEFINITIONS

Key Word	Definition	Picture Clue
	Freeing people from slavery	
	A part of a person's body that does not work right which can make it hard to get things done	
	The mixing of a racial or religious group into a community	
	Refusing to move from a building, doorway, or seat, to bring about change	
	Treating people badly because of the color of their skin or the place from which they cam	

George Washington

He led the fight for freedom from England and helped establish a new country.

Abraham Lincoln

He was the United States President who helped free enslaved African Americans.

Susan B. Anthony

She led the struggle to give women equal rights, including the right to vote.

Helen Keller

She overcame disabilities and worked to help others who were blind and deaf.

Jackie Robinson

He was the first African American player in the major leagues of baseball.
His actions helped to bring about other opportunities for African Americans.

Martin Luther King, Jr.

He was an African American minister who worked so that all people would be treated fairly. He led peaceful marches and gave speeches.

ECONOMICS

Social Studies Standards of Learning

STANDARD 2.7

The student will describe natural resources (water, soil, wood, and coal), human resources (people at work), and capital resources (machines, tools, and buildings).

STANDARD 2.8

The student will distinguish between the use of barter and the use of money in the exchange for goods and services.

STANDARD 2.9

The student will explain that scarcity (limited resources) requires people to make choices about producing and consuming goods and services.

Essential Questions

STANDARD 2.7

• What are natural, human, and capital resources?

STANDARD 2.8

• What is the difference between using barter and using money in exchange for goods and services?

STANDARD 2.9

• What is scarcity?
• What is a consumer?
• What is a producer?
• Why do people have to make economic choices?

(continued on the next page)

Learning At Home

One of the concepts discussed in this standard is the use of coins, paper bills, and checks. Show your child examples of all of these and discuss how you use them every day. Explain that you deposit money in the bank and then write checks to use the money. The bank keeps a record of money received and spent. Children need to understand that the bank does not give you the money. You earn the money and the bank keeps it safe. You cannot write a check if you haven't deposited the money. This can be a hard concept for young children to grasp.

• BECOME A COIN COLLECTOR

Spend some time looking at the various types of coins and paper bills. What are the differences? Who are the people pictured on each coin? Why are the coins different colors? Originally the penny was made of copper and the nickel was made of a metal called nickel. The dime was made of silver. Silver was more valuable than nickel so the silver dime was smaller. The quarter was also made of silver and since it was worth more than the dime, it was larger. Coins today are no longer made of pure metal but the shapes and colors remain the same.

Between 1999 and 2009, the U.S. Mint released a new quarter design every 10 weeks designed to celebrate our 50 states. There were 50 different quarter designs released during that ten year period. Your child may enjoy looking for and collecting these quarters.

All coins are dated when they are produced. Look for examples of coins which were made the year of your child's birth. They might make an interesting keepsake in the future. You can learn more by visiting the website of the United States Mint at **http://www.usmint.gov/.**

• WORKING AND SAVING

Money is used in exchange for goods and services. Give your child a short list of chores and reward their completion each week with a small allowance. Your child can use the money to begin making decisions about spending and saving. You may wish to encourage the use of envelopes or savings jars to help your child create a budget. Many authorities suggest teaching children to use a three part system. Using this method, children divide their allowance into three parts: to spend now, to save for later, and to use to help others. (continued on the next page)

Social Studies Standards of Learning

STANDARDS 2.7-2.9

Essential Knowledge

TERMS TO KNOW
- **Natural resources:** Materials that come directly from nature
- **Human resources:** People working to produce goods and services
- **Capital resources:** Goods made by people and used to produce other goods and services

EXAMPLES OF RESOURCES
- **Natural**: Water, soil, wood, coal
- **Human:** Farmers, miners, builders, painters
- **Capital:** Hammers, computers, trucks, lawn mowers, factory buildings

TERMS TO KNOW
- **Barter:** The exchange of goods and services without the use of money
- **Money:** Coins, paper bills, and checks used in exchange for goods and services
- **Scarcity:** Not being able to meet all wants at the same time because resources are limited
- **Consumer:** A person who uses goods and services
- **Producer:** A person who uses resources to make goods and/or provide services. People must make economic choices because resources and goods and services are scarce (limited).

Learning At Home

• TALK ABOUT YOUR JOB

Talk with your children about the work you do. Do you produce a good or provide a service for others? Whatever job you perform, when you are at work you are a producer. When you purchase items, you are a consumer.

Children need to grasp that the terms "producer" and "consumer" relate to what you are doing and not who you are. Each person plays both roles but at different times. Try to use these words with your child as you describe what you are doing throughout the day.

• BUDGET CRUNCHING

Children learn by example. Talk with your child about the financial decisions you make. Discuss the things your family needs and compare them to the things you want. All families need to buy food and pay for housing expenses. Water and electricity are needs which must come before TV services and toys. Be sure your child understands that you do not get everything you want. Even adults have to make choices and these choices can be very difficult.

• LET'S GO SHOPPING!

Take your child with you on shopping trips. Have him or her help you compare prices of similar items and decide which would be the best use of your money. Be sure to allow your child the experience of purchasing small items and receiving change.

• BE "RESOURCEFUL"

We use resources every day.

Human resources are always people.
Natural resources come directly from nature.
Capital resources are things which people make and which are used to make other goods and services.

As you prepare dinner, talk about the human, capital, and natural resources which are in play. The person cooking the dinner is the human resource. The stove, microwave, plates, bowls, spoons, and other cooking tools are the capital resources. The water you use comes directly from nature. It is a natural resource. Have your child look for examples of these resources in your community.

Policemen, firemen, doctors, farmers, builders, miners, and painters are all examples of human resources. Work together with your child to list family members and the ways that they contribute to the community as human resources.

Buildings, computers, hammers, construction equipment, scissors, lawn mowers, and other tools are capital resources. Look around your home for other examples.

Water, soil, wood, and coal come directly from nature and are examples of natural resources. Talk about the different ways that natural resources are used. What are some ways we can protect our natural resources? How can we work to keep our water clean?

THE BANK OF TREATS

FIRST NATIONAL BANK OF TREATS

DATE _____

PAY TO THE
ORDER OF _____

_____ PIECES OF CANDY

_____
SIGNED

FIRST NATIONAL BANK OF TREATS

DATE _____

PAY TO THE
ORDER OF _____

_____ PIECES OF CANDY

_____
SIGNED

FIRST NATIONAL BANK OF TREATS

DATE _____

PAY TO THE
ORDER OF _____

_____ PIECES OF CANDY

_____
SIGNED

BE RESOURCEFUL!

Name _____

Use the words in the Word Box to fill in the boxes. Remember, words may be used more than once!
Use your own words to fill in the last column.

wood	truck	lawn mower	soil	hammer	computer	water	coal

HUMAN RESOURCES	use these NATURAL RESOURCES	use these CAPITAL RESOURCES	to:

ARE YOU A PRODUCER OR A CONSUMER?

NAME _____

I AM A PRODUCER WHEN I...   **I AM A CONSUMER WHEN I...**

WHAT WILL YOU CHOOSE?

 CANDY

 HEALTH CARE

 ELECTRICITY

 COMPUTER

 TELEPHONE

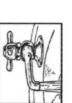 TRANSPORTATION

Making economic choices is hard. Think about your family's needs and wants. How would you spend your family's money? Decide which items are the most important. Then cut them out and place them in order of need. Number 1 should be the most important.

 WATER

 CLOTHING

 TOYS

 VACATION

 ELECTRICITY

FOOD

NAME _____

1

2

3

4

5

6

7

8

9

10

IT'S YOUR CHOICE!

Name _____

You have just received ten dollars for your birthday. How will you spend it?

How many **different** items can you buy?
Do you have anything left over to save?

Here are your choices.

2 candy bars....$1.00
5 baseball cards.....$1.50
1 movie ticket.....$7.00
1 slice pizza.....$2.50
1 soft drink.....$1.25
1 ice cream cone.....$1.75
1 book.....$3.50
1 bag popcorn.....$1.00
1 stuffed animal.....$6.00
1 box of 48 crayons.....$2.00
2 packs of gum.....50¢
1 donut......75¢
1 sticker......25¢

MY CHOICES ARE:	AMOUNT SPENT:
1.	
2.	
3.	
4.	
5.	
6.	
7.	
8.	
9.	
10.	
TOTAL SPENT	

VOCABULARY DEFINITIONS

Key Word	Definition	Picture Clue
	Materials that come directly from nature	
	People working to produce goods and services	
	Goods made by people and used to produce other goods and services	
	The exchange of goods and services without the use of money	
	Coins, paper bills, and checks used in exchange for goods and services	
	Not being able to meet all wants at the same time because resources are limited	
	A person who uses goods and services	
	A person who uses resources to make goods and/or provide services	